HISTORY ACTIVITY

Ancient EGYPT

Autumn
Publishing

LIFE BY THE NILE

Over 5,000 years ago, in the heart of the North African desert, towns, cities and farms sprang up around the green, grassy banks of the river Nile. From 3000 BCE to 30 BCE, these places made up the powerful kingdom of Ancient Egypt, ruled by kings and queens called pharaohs. Read the clues and find the matching stickers to fill in the gaps on the map.

Cleopatra was the last pharaoh of Egypt. She and her Roman boyfriend Antony fought to save Egypt from the Romans (another ancient society). When they lost, Egypt became part of the Roman Empire, marking an end to 3,000 years of Egyptian history. Way to go, Cleo.

Ancient Egyptians invented papyrus, a type of paper made out of papyrus reeds. They cut the plants' stems into thin strips, which they wove together and dried in the sun.

Ancient Egyptians wrote in hieroglyphs (pictures that mean sounds or words). No one could read them for thousands of years, until archaeologists (people who dig stuff up) found the Rosetta Stone, with hieroglyphs translated into other ancient languages.

In 330 BCE, Alexander the Great (a Greek king) turned up in Egypt, kicked out the pharaoh, made his friend pharaoh instead (Ptolemy I), named a city after himself, then left.

Pharaohs liked to be buried in style, so they built huge stone pyramids to house their tombs. Three of the largest are at Giza.

The Sphinx, a huge stone sculpture with the head of a human and the body of a lion, guards the pyramids at Giza.

The Bent Pyramid is one of the earliest pyramids, built on the orders of a pharaoh called Sneferu.

Heliopolis (Greek for 'sun city'), was sacred to the sun god Ra. A massive obelisk built in his honour still stands there today.

ALEXANDRIA

ROSETTA

HELIOPOLIS

MEMPHIS

GIZA

Ancient Egyptians built huge temples, like this one at Luxor, in which to worship their many gods and goddesses.

● LUXOR

● THEBES

● VALLEY OF THE KINGS

TRUE OR FALSE? The Great Pyramid of Giza held the title of tallest building in the world for more than 4,000 years.

Once a year, the river Nile flooded. Silt and mud washed onto the riverbanks, making them perfect for farming.

There weren't many roads in Ancient Egypt. Instead, ships carried people, food and other goods up and down the country.

When pharaohs were fed up of building pyramids, they dug tombs into solid rock at the Valley of the Kings instead. This made tombs (slightly) safer from grave-robbers.

QUIZ: Which weighs more, the obelisk of Heliopolis or 20 elephants?

Answers on page 16

People took mud from the riverbanks, shaped it and baked it in the sun to make bricks to build houses.

Grain was kept in large, shared granaries or store-houses. That way, if the crops failed for a year, the grain could be given out fairly to everyone.

Beyond the lush, green riverbanks were miles of hot, dry, sandy desert. Determined pharaohs would make expeditions to attack neighbouring civilisations in Nubia in the south and Libya in the west.

QUIZ: Why did the Bent Pyramid have wonky sides?
a. Because Sheferu thought straight lines were ugly.
b. The builder did his sums wrong.
c. It was straight when it was built, but over thousands of years, bits of it have fallen off.

CITY LIFE

Many people in Ancient Egypt lived in cities close to the river, away from the scorching desert. Cities were important places where people could buy food and other goods, visit temples and work in lots of different jobs, from mummy makers to government scribes. Festivals for gods were a good excuse for a day off. Can you spot all the things in the list in this celebratory scene?

QUIZ: Lots of fruits and vegetables grew in the rich soil of the Nile, but can you spot the tropical fruits you wouldn't have found in Ancient Egypt?

People bathed most days in the waters of the Nile.

Rich Egyptians mixed wax with perfume and wore it in cones on their heads. As the wax melted in the warm sun, the cone gave off scent. Stylish.

CAN YOU SPOT?
• A statue of Bastet, the cat goddess • 16 cats • 2 children's toys
• The oldest board game in the world • Ancient Egyptian perfume

Whenever statues of gods were moved, there was a grand procession with priests and acrobats.

People had shrines in their homes for household gods and dead relatives. They would leave food out for them every day (and sometimes help them eat it).

Because it was so hot, rich Egyptians shaved their heads and wore wigs instead. These wigs could be extravagantly styled.

TRUE OR FALSE?
Some people were so fond of their ancient curling tongs, they were buried with them.

TRUE OR FALSE?
The water in the Nile got pretty mucky, so most people drank beer.

Answers on page 16

WHO'S THAT GOD?

Ancient Egyptians had a god for just about everything. The palace painters are working on portraits of a few of the 2,000 gods. Some of their names have already been translated, but others have letters missing. Can you use the hieroglyph key to decipher the rest of the gods' names? Then add the missing gods from your sticker sheet.

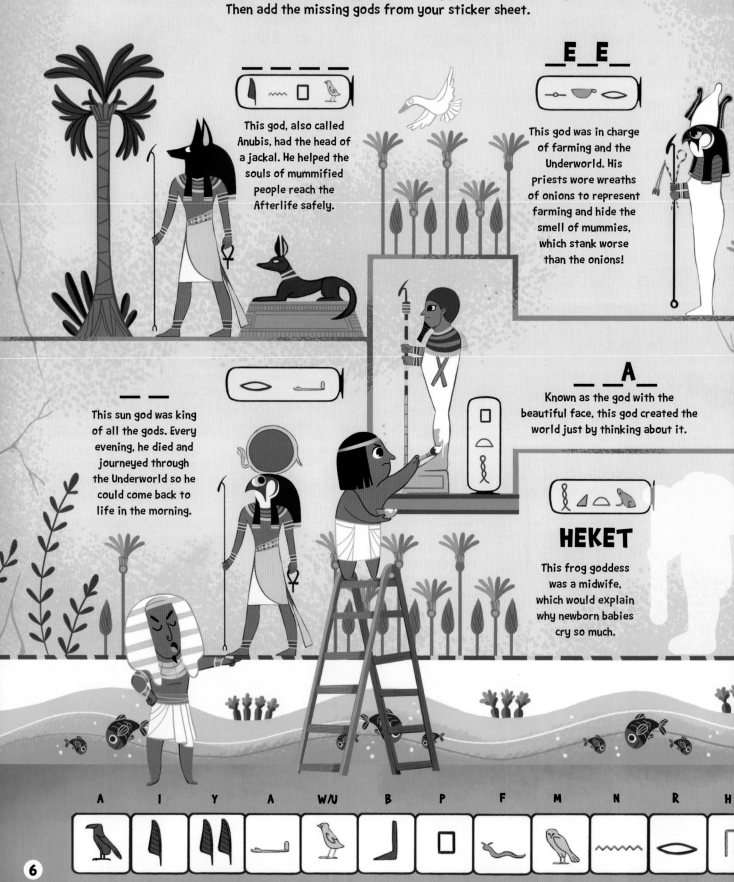

This god, also called Anubis, had the head of a jackal. He helped the souls of mummified people reach the Afterlife safely.

_ _ E _ E _

This god was in charge of farming and the Underworld. His priests wore wreaths of onions to represent farming and hide the smell of mummies, which stank worse than the onions!

_ _ _

This sun god was king of all the gods. Every evening, he died and journeyed through the Underworld so he could come back to life in the morning.

_ _A _

Known as the god with the beautiful face, this god created the world just by thinking about it.

HEKET

This frog goddess was a midwife, which would explain why newborn babies cry so much.

A	I	Y	W/U	B	P	F	M	N	R	H

_ O _ E _

Who would you trust to protect you from the River Nile? A crocodile, of course! This snappy god also protected pharaohs from harm.

Puzzling pictograms

Some hieroglyphs are pictures of the things they represent. Find the stickers on your sticker sheet and match them to the meanings below.

dung beetle   bee   walking

bird   frog   sun

Answers on page 16

Ancient Egyptians also worshipped cats, as they were sacred to the cat goddess Bastet.

Odd god

Gods' names were written in holders, or cartouches. Write your name (or make up a new one) in hieroglyphs in the cartouche, then draw yourself as a god.

TRUE OR FALSE?
This god had a city called Crocodilopolis named after him.

HORUS

God of war and hunting, this falcon-headed god was the son of Osiris (though there isn't much of a family resemblance).

OSIRIS

This god always looks a bit green. That's because he's dead. His brother chopped him up and hid bits of his body across Egypt. Luckily his wife managed to find them all and stitch him back together!

Answers on page 16

H	CK	S	S	SH	K	K	G	T	CH	D	J

MUMMY MAKING

When rich Ancient Egyptians died, they had their bodies mummified. They believed this would let them take their bodies with them into the Afterlife. Mummifying a body was quite complicated. Can you put the instructions below into the correct order? Remember, don't try this at home!

A.

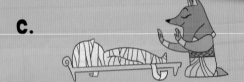

Cover the body with special salt for 70 days. You can use this time to read an improving book. The Book of the Dead is pretty popular.

B.

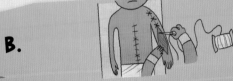

Stuff the body with sand and linen to make it look more life-like. Some people tip extra if you pack in extra muscles.

C.

Wrap the body in linen bandages. Say some prayers and admire a job well done.

D.

Poke a metal hook up Mummy-to-be's nose. Wiggle the hook to mush up the brain, then let the brain stream out the nose like lumpy jelly.

E.

Rinse out Mummy's insides with wine and spices. You probably shouldn't drink the wine afterwards (not if you don't want to get pickled yourself).

F.

Open up Mummy's chest and chop out the organs. Let them dry out for a few days, then sort them into canopic jars.

Answer on page 16

Mummy masks

Sculptors and painters made golden masks to place over the mummies' faces (most people don't look their best after 70 days pickled with salt). Use your stickers to create masks for these three mummies.

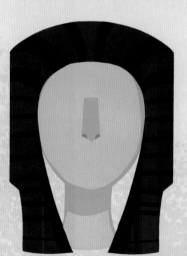

PRESS-OUT PYRAMID

Thousands of builders travelled across Egypt to build the pyramids. Each pyramid took years of backbreaking work. Huge stones were dragged across the desert, then somehow lifted to the top of the pyramid. Some people think the builders made a massive ramp, others think they used huge levers to lift the stones. Luckily, you don't have to do any of that to build a pyramid. Just pull out the page opposite and fold along the dotted lines, gently at first. The green lines fold away from you. The blue lines fold towards you. Keep folding along the lines until the pyramid pulls into place. Finally, press out the characters, slot them into their bases and arrange them around the pyramid.

senet tokens
Pages 10–11

Life by the Nile Pages 2–3

Who's that god? Pages 6–7

Mummy making Page 8

Canopic chaos

Each organ was put into its own canopic jar to be looked after by a specific god.
Can you follow the lines to help this priest sort the organs into the correct jars?

1.   2.   3.   4.

A.
B.   C.
D.

A. LUNGS
B. LIVER
C. STOMACH
D. INTESTINES

TRUE OR FALSE?
Mummy makers
threw away the
hearts because
they didn't
think they were
important.

QUIZ: The word sarcophagus literally means
'flesh-eater'. Why did it get this name?
a. People believed if you didn't mummify a body
properly, it would come back to life and eat you.
b. The earliest coffins were made of limestone,
which would dissolve the dead bodies.
c. Mummies would attract jackals and wolves,
who would try to eat the tasty dead flesh.

Answers on page 16

SENET

At 5,000 years old, senet is the oldest board game in the world. It was played by everyone in Ancient Egypt. Pharaohs were buried with sets carved out of precious jade stone, while townspeople scratched boards into stone floors. People believed that you could play the game after you died to help your soul make its way through the Afterlife. Press out the tokens and follow the instructions to play with a friend.

1.	2.	3.	4.	5.
20.	19.	18.	17.	16.
21.	22.	23.	24.	25.

How to play

The aim is to remove all of your tokens from the board before your opponent does. Press out the game tokens (5 each) from the press-out sheet. Set them up so player 1 has tokens on squares 1, 3, 5, 7 and 9, and player 2 has tokens on squares 2, 4, 6, 8 and 10. Take turns to throw the senet sticks and make your move.

You can jump over other tokens, but you can't land on a square that already holds one of your tokens. You can capture your opponent's tokens by landing on them. Move captured tokens back to the square your token was in at the start of your turn.

If you can't land on a square (because it already holds one of your tokens), move a token backwards instead. If you can't move a token backwards, move a token back to the start.

Senet sticks

Make senet sticks out of four lolly-pop sticks or pieces of card. Colour them so each stick has one black side and one white side. When it's your turn, throw the sticks gently in the air. How the sticks land decides how many squares you move.

	Move a token one square, then throw again.
	Move a token two squares and end your turn.
	Move a token three squares and end your turn.
	Move a token four squares, then throw again.
	Move a token five squares, then throw again.

6.	7.	8.	9.	10.
15.	14.	13.	12.	11.
26.	27.	28.	29.	30. Finish

Special squares

HOUSE OF HAPPINESS
Every token must land on the House of Happiness in order to move past. You cannot jump over it.

HOUSE OF WATER
If your token lands on the House of Water, move it back to the House of Rebirth and lose your turn.

HOUSE OF THREE TRUTHS
When you land on this square, throw the sticks again. Throw three white sticks to remove the token from the board.

HOUSE OF REBIRTH
If your token is captured on any other special square, move your token back to the House of Rebirth.

HOUSE OF RE-ATOUM
When you land on this square, throw the sticks again. Throw two white sticks to remove the token from the board.

HOUSE OF RA
When you land on this square, throw the sticks again. Throw one white stick to remove your token, and move one of your opponent's tokens to the House of Rebirth.

A PHARAOH'S TOMB

When a pharaoh died, it was officially a Big Deal. The next pharaoh gave them a proper send-off and packed their tomb full of everything they'd need for the next life, from tiny model servants and soldiers to mummified pets to keep them company. Use stickers to fill up this pharaoh's tomb.

TRUE OR FALSE?
Ancient Egyptians put curses on
tombs and filled them with traps
to stop grave-robbers.

Answer on page 16

Some of the grave-robbers were the builders
who made the tombs. They knew all the weak
spots (and sometimes knocked a few holes
in the walls for good measure).

13

JOURNEY OF THE DEAD

Congratulations! You, a humble Ancient Egyptian farmer, have died in the desert! The hot, dry weather has naturally mummified your body, so even though your poor family couldn't afford a fancy mummification, you still get to go to the Afterlife. Unfortunately, you haven't got a copy of the Book of the Dead, so your trip through Duat (the Underworld) will be a bit more tricky. Can you make your way safely to paradise?

Start

Another stroke of luck! You die at sunset so you hitch a ride with Ra on his nightly trip through Duat. In his boat, you see a page of the Book of the Dead. Do you...

... steal it? It could be useful later.

... leave it where it is? Stealing is wrong.

You sail on through murk and gloom, until you reach a fork in the river. Do you go towards...

Your soul burns to a crisp. Bad luck.

Did you get the gift of staying cool in hot places?

No

Yes

Perfect. Carry on towards...

Good call. This is the friendly snake deity. It's hard to tell because he looks like an unfriendly snake demon. He carries you safely in his mouth to...

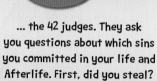

... the 42 judges. They ask you questions about which sins you committed in your life and Afterlife. First, did you steal?

You tumble forever in eternal darkness.

No

Yes

Do you want to lie about it?

Yes

No

The Swallower of Shades devours you.

... the demons with warlike faces?

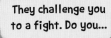 ... fight?

They challenge you to a fight. Do you...

... use the page from the Book of the Dead?

... lie to them and say you're a fierce warrior?

They rip apart your soul. Obviously. They're demons.

Subdued, the demons give you the gift of staying cool in the hottest places in Duat. See, they're not so bad after all.

... the gods who belong to the Sunshine?

They give you the gift of light in dark places. That's nice of them.

... towards the Pits of Flame?

You sail along the river until you reach another fork. Do you go...

... into the mouth of a giant snake?

... into the Fathomless Ravines?

Your heart is devoured by the man-eating part-crocodile, part-hippo, part-lion monster. Shame. You nearly made it.

 Finish

Yes

Now, your heart will be weighed against the Feather of Truth. Have you lied at all in your journey?

No

Congratulations! You've reached the glorious Field of Reeds. You can spend the rest of eternity ploughing the fields and sowing crops for the pharaoh, just as you did when you were alive. Bliss.

ANSWERS

PAGES 2–3: LIFE BY THE NILE

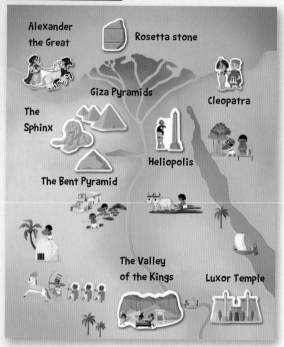

Alexander the Great
Rosetta stone
Giza Pyramids
Cleopatra
The Sphinx
The Bent Pyramid
Heliopolis
The Valley of the Kings
Luxor Temple

QUIZ: b. It was the first pyramid with smooth sides (instead of rocky steps), and the builder wasn't quite sure how to do the maths. Halfway through being built, the pyramid started to collapse, so they had to change the angles.

QUIZ: The obelisk weighs more!

TRUE OR FALSE? True!

PAGES 4–5: CITY LIFE

QUIZ: Bananas and pineapples weren't found in Ancient Egypt.

TRUE OR FALSE? True, but the beer was pretty grotty, too. They had to drink it out of really long straws to filter out all the lumps.

TRUE OR FALSE? True. Archaeologists have found golden, decorated curling tongs in ancient tombs. Just because you're dead, doesn't mean you can't look fabulous!

PAGES 6–7: WHO'S THAT GOD?

INPU
SEKER
SOBEK
RA
PTAH
HORUS
HEKET
OSIRIS

PUZZLING PICTOGRAMS

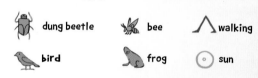

dung beetle
bee
walking
bird
frog
sun

TRUE OR FALSE? True!

PAGES 8–9: MUMMY MAKING

Order: D. F. E. A. B. C.

CANOPIC CHAOS

A – 2, B – 3, C – 1, D – 4.

TRUE OR FALSE? False! The heart was very important! It got mummified and put back inside the body so the mummy wouldn't lose it in the Afterlife. The brain, on the other hand, went straight in the bin.

QUIZ: b.

PAGES 12–13: A PHARAOH'S TOMB

FALSE. This was a myth invented by early archaeologists when they found the ancient tombs, then kept going by Hollywood movies. Grave diggers were a problem, though, and the royal family employed guards to keep watch and catch thieves.